BATTLE BOOKS

ARNHEM

Gary Smailes

Illustrated by David Cousens

For Ben —— G.S.

First published in 2011
by Franklin Watts

Text © Gary Smailes 2011
Illustrations © David Cousens 2011

The author and illustrator have asserted their rights in
accordance with the Copyright, Designs and Patents Act, 1988.

A CIP catalogue record for this book
is available from the British Library.

ISBN: 978 1 4451 0113 2

1 3 5 7 9 10 8 6 4 2

Printed in Great Britain

Franklin Watts is a division of Hachette Children's Books,
an Hachette UK company.
www.hachette.co.uk

"When I went to school my history lessons were all about learning the names of kings and endless lists of dates. *Yawn*. But exciting history asks: How did people live and how did they die? How did they feel? Were they just like us or more like aliens from another planet? Those are the questions that *Battle Books* explore. I wish Gary Smailes and his books had been around when I went to school."
— **Terry Deary, author of *Horrible Histories***

BATTLE BOOKS

Prepare to fight your own battle...

Start the story, then choose which numbered paragraph to follow. Go to that paragraph to continue on and see if you can accomplish your mission by making it to Arnhem, and capturing and holding the bridge there.

YOU are a Lieutenant in the 2nd Parachute Battalion and command a platoon of men. Your platoon consists of three rifle sections, each containing ten men; that is thirty soldiers in total. These sections are each lead by a different Corporal, who is under your command.

CHAIN OF COMMAND

1st Parachute Brigade (Brigadier Lathbury)

2nd Parachute Battalion (Lieutenant Colonel Frost)

A Company (Major Tatham-Warter)

4 Platoon (Lieutenant YOU)

1 Section: 10 men
(Corporal Revie)

2 Section: 10 men
(Corporal Venables)

3 Section: 10 men
(Corporal Ramsey)

WEAPONS

Rifles

Most of your men are armed with Lee Enfield bolt action rifles, which use .303 bullets carried in magazines of ten. These are accurate and dependable rifles.

Machine guns

Some of your men have Sten (left) and Thompson (right) sub-machine-guns. But the most powerful machine gun you have available is the Bren gun (below). You have two of these MGs, which fire .303 bullets at a rapid rate of fire. They can be lethal when used correctly.

Anti-tank

If you come across German armoured vehicles then you might be able order your men to use a PIAT anti-tank weapon (right). This is fired by a single man, but needs two to operate effectively, and has only a very short range.

If tanks become a real problem then you might be able to call up the 6-pounder (above), which is a cannon designed to destroy tanks. It is very good at its job.

2-inch mortar (not shown)
Infantry attacks are often supported by 2-inch mortars. This weapon is a long tube that fires mortar bombs. It takes two men to fire and is effective against infantry in the open or in cover.

It is 1944, and Hitler's Nazi German forces occupy most of Europe. On 6th June, in a carefully planned attack to recapture France called Operation Overlord (D-Day), thousands of Allied troops attacked the French shores in Normandy. It was a success and the German forces were pushed back to The Netherlands.

It was hoped that after the attack Hitler's men would give up, but in the months after D-Day it has become clear they are still ready for a fight.

British leaders have now come up with a daring plan, called Operation Market Garden. It aims to defeat the Germans and end the war by Christmas 1944. British and American troops will avoid the strong Nazi defences on the German border and attack through The Netherlands instead.

If this plan is to succeed, several bridges across important rivers and canals must be secured. If the Germans are able to blow up just one of these bridges, the whole attack could fail.

The bridges are all deep in enemy territory and the only way to get near them is to use paratroopers. The job of capturing and holding the bridges has been handed to three groups. The American 101st Screaming Eagles are to capture the bridges around Eindhoven. The American 82nd are to capture the bridges at Grave and Nijmegen, whilst the 1st Parachute Brigade British Red Devils have been tasked with taking the last bridge at Arnhem. They must hold the bridge until 30 Corp, a collection of tanks and infantry, can fight their way up the narrow road which runs all the way from the border of Belgium to Arnhem.

You command a platoon of British paratroopers who form part of 1st British Airborne Division. You will parachute into a field ten kilometres from Arnhem at Landing Zone X. You must fight your way through German troops, capture the bridge at Arnhem and then hold it until 30 Corp arrive to support you...

Now go to section 1.

1

The drone of the plane's two wing-mounted engines makes it almost impossible for you to think. You are standing in a line of paratroopers, the men behind you chatter nervously, pushing close. Your pack and weapons are weighing you down. The smell of aviation fuel is overwhelming and you fight the urge to be sick.

Suddenly the side door in the fuselage is pushed open. You glance out of the rectangular window to your right; the camouflaged wing of the plane blocks most of your view, but you can make out the patchwork of light green fields and dark green wooded areas below. Snaking between them is a thin silver line that is the River Rhine.

The red jump light by the door blinks on – five minutes to the jump. The men surrounding you fall silent. The droning engines seem louder now. Everyone shuffles forward, pushing you towards the open doorway.

Suddenly the green light comes on and a bell rings out.

The dispatcher screams "GO!" and the first paratrooper in the line is thrust from the plane into the open space beyond. One by one paratroopers are dispatched. Then it is your turn. You pause, letting the cold wind whip at your face.

"GO!"

A hand pushes you firmly in the back and you are out. The noise of the rushing air deafens you and before you can react your parachute is pulled open with a jolt. Suddenly all is calm. You look up to see your chute is open, its huge dirty yellow canopy floating high above you.

Below you can see the Landing Zone, just like on the maps you studied last night. A rectangle of farmland is your target and you can already see other parachutes and gliders on the ground.

You fumble with the catch on your kitbag, release it and then lower it down on its long rope. Your training kicks in. Head down, shoulders round, feet together… The ground rushes closer and you land hard, knocking the wind from your lungs. You lie motionless for a second, eyes closed. No pain, you are OK! Then you are up on your feet, fumbling with your chute harness and collecting your kitbag.

Your orders are to join up with your men at the south-east side of the Landing Zone. It is supposed to be marked by yellow smoke. Yet, as you scan the chaotic scene of thousands of paratroopers, you can only see yellow smoke to the north.

◊ *If you want to head north towards the yellow smoke, go to 59.*
◊ *If you want to head south-east to the prearranged meeting point, go to 46.*

Sunday, night...

You find Major Tatham-Warter, surrounded by paratroopers, positioned under Arnhem Bridge. The road section stretches out high above your head. The Major turns as you approach.

"Ah, just the man. I need you to capture this end of the bridge." As he speaks he points to the road above your heads. You explain that you only have a section of men with you, but the Major insists there will be little German resistance.

◊ *If you wish to carry out the Major's orders, go to 15.*

◊ *If you wish to try to explain you need more men, go to 67.*

Tuesday, morning...

You point in the direction you last saw a tank, which was destroying the platoon house to the north. Frank nods, and you both bob down the street in that direction, ducking from doorway to doorway. The wide, cobbled street is flanked by large town houses. At the end is a line of trees, and behind these, the wide river.

Frank stops at the junction of two streets and tucks in against a wall. You do the same.

"Tank," he whispers, "just around the corner."

◊ *To attack the tank, go to 45.*

◊ *If you don't want to risk an attack, go to 93.*

4 *Sunday, night...*

You spring to your feet and shout for your men to retreat. In the middle of the road you are exposed and bullets slice through the air around you. The German machine gun continues to fire. 2 Section are slow to react. You kick Corporal Venables, the nearest man, into action. He jumps to his feet – ordering his men off the bridge.

You sprint across to 1 Section on your left, but they are already moving back along the bridge. The machine gun fire is now more random – the darkness protecting your retreat. As you jog away from the pillbox you see at least six paratrooper bodies on the ground – one of them is Corporal Ramsey. You are the last man off the bridge.

The Major is waiting on the road below the bridge. You explain that the attack failed and he just nods and thanks you. You tell him that there are bodies of paratroopers on the bridge and ask his permission to mount another attack to return the bodies. The Major looks you in the eye and simply says no, ordering you back to your platoon house.

◊ *If you wish to disobey the order and take your men to get the bodies, go to 96.*

◊ *If you wish to do as you are told and return to the house, go to 88.*

5 *Monday, morning...*

The German attack speeds onto the bridge, pushing past the burned-out trucks. At the front are fast motorcycles, then about twenty armoured cars and behind these are half-tracks packed full of German troops. You are surprised to see British artillery shells dropping onto the bridge. They are accurate, blasting the motorcycles but they have little effect on the armoured vehicles. The column snakes along the road, past the blackened framework. The house is almost level with the bridge road, and the German vehicles are no more than 100 metres away. You wait until the first few armoured cars are level before you fire.

Rifles, machine guns and anti-tank weapons fire onto the bridge from all around. The lead armoured car explodes and the second car rams into it, blocking the road. You are lying on the floor with the PIAT pointing out of the hole in the wall. You line up the sights on the third armoured car in the line and squeeze the large, square trigger. The anti-tank weapon shudders as the projectile is launched and the barrel pushes violently back against your body. You watch as the bomb loops out of the window and towards the bridge. Your aim is poor and the charge drops short, thudding into the road with a small explosion.

Luckily the armoured cars are hit by other PIAT teams, and the road is soon filled with burning vehicles, dead German soldiers and immobile armoured cars. But the Germans just keep coming. Half-tracks now try to push their way past the wrecks. You can see that these are packed with German infantrymen, who start to jump out and deploy on the road.

◊ *To fire on the German infantry, go to 65.*
◊ *To fire on the half-tracks, go to 32.*

---

6 *Sunday, 7:30 p.m. – ½ hour to sunset...*
You slowly move round to face the other direction, being careful not to expose yourself to the machine gunner's fire. You crawl and sprint between walls, houses and trees to get back to Major Tatham-Warter. He is standing outside the three houses near the underpass. Beside him is Lt. Col. John Frost, the battalion commander. Frost has a magnificently bushy moustache, shrugged shoulders and seems small next to the lanky Major.

You jog up to the officers and explain the situation ahead. Frost listens, carefully stroking his moustache as you speak. When you have finished he thanks you and turns to B Company commander Major Crawley who is standing close by. Frost simply points in the direction of the German machine gun and says, "Deal with it."

Crawley salutes and quickly disappears. Frost and Major Tatham-Warter soon head off after him.

In the distance you can still hear the splutter of the German machine gun. About 15 minutes later, gunfire breaks out to your left. It appears B Company are attacking along the railway line.

You are sitting on the wall outside the houses when Lt. Col. Frost reappears along the road. He looks worried. There is no sign of Major Tatham-Warter.

"OK, let's get moving," orders Frost.

It is clear Frost will be joining your advance. You pause for a moment unsure what to do next.

◊ *If you feel uncomfortable with the battalion commander at your side, go to 63, to tell him your worries.*

◊ *If you wish to do as Frost orders, go to 74.*

7 *Sunday, night...*

You point to the hut and the soldier with the flame-thrower nods. Suddenly the black night is illuminated by a rod of yellow flame. It gushes from the flame-thrower nozzle over the gap and onto the bridge. The flame hits the nearest small wooden hut, setting it alight.

The soldier stops firing and watches the hut. At first it is a small fire, but it quickly spreads. Suddenly there is a huge explosion as the hut disintegrates, throwing burning wood across the bridge. The paint of the nearby arches catches alight and soon the whole metal framework is burning.

You send the two soldiers away and settle in for the night, watching the fire tickle away at the bridge. There is no chance it will collapse but it will take some time to burn off all the paint. After a while you fall asleep.

You are woken a few hours later by a huge explosion and looking out over the bridge you see that a few German trucks have tried to cross over the still burning structure. Somehow they had caught alight and are now just burning hulks in the middle of the road. You soon fall asleep once again.

◊ *Go to 41.*

8   *Wednesday, morning...*

You quickly secure the bridge and tell your men to spread out and wait for the German counterattack. You try not to think about what would happen if a bullet hits the explosives on the bridge. Under the bridge you use the two tall concrete pillars for cover. You tell your men that the Germans could come from any direction.

When the attack does come it is from your right and begins with a few poorly aimed shots that ping wildly between the pillars. You struggle to see where the Germans are firing from, and try to scan the surrounding houses. Suddenly the Germans burst onto the river road.

You squeeze the trigger of your Sten, spraying bullets towards the Germans. But then your world goes fuzzy and you slump to the ground with the chilling chatter of a heavy German machine gun ringing in your ears.

◊   *Go to 52.*

---

9   *Wednesday, morning...*

You return to the platoon house and collect up the remaining men. What was once a plattoon of more than thirty men, is reduced to just eight paratroopers still able to fight. You tell the men the situation is desperate, but you have been asked to stop the Germans from blowing up the bridge.

You give the men fifteen minutes to prepare and then set out south. You move quickly, passing an immobilised German tank on your way to the river – its gun poking in the air at an unnatural angle. When you get to the river road you turn left.

Ahead you can see under the bridge as it rises across the river. However, standing around at the base of the tall concrete pillars that support the structure is a group of about twenty German soldiers.

◊ If you wish to launch an attack against the Germans, go to 47.
◊ If you feel that you are outnumbered and retreat would be the best option, go to 23.

Tuesday, morning...
You swing to the right and enter the room. A cupboard has been pushed against one window, and a group of chairs against another window on the opposite wall. There are two German soldiers at the first window.

You squeeze the trigger of your Sten. The Germans are only paces away. The bullets rip into the first German, throwing him back. You swing round and strafe the second German, who slumps to the floor.

You turn and run into the other room. A German soldier lies dead in the centre of the room, blood covering his face. The body of a second dead German lies across a window sill. Lying next to the German on the floor is Corporal Venables.

You rush in and duck down next to the Corporal. There is an oozing patch of deep red on the front of his khaki jacket. You fiddle with this uniform to reveal a large hole in the man's chest. It is pumping blood at an alarming rate. You pull his head into your lap and carefully stroke the dying man's hair from his face. Your touch causes his eyes to flicker open and a faint smile flashes onto his lips.

"My pocket," he says, his voice just a rasp.

You delve into the front pocket of his jacket and inside you find two items. The first is a faded, and now bloodstained, picture of a pretty young girl. In her arms is a small baby. You also gather up a letter with the name Mary and Baby Joe scrawled on the front.

"Make sure my missus and the little 'un get the letter," says Venables. You nod, unable to speak. The Corporal's body then goes weak and you feel his last breath slip away.

Tears well in your eyes and you cannot help but cry as you sit on the dirty floor with your dead friend cradled in your lap.

◊ *Go to 18.*

11 *Wednesday, morning...*

You rise from the floor and step carefully around the injured men, heading towards the door. You push the medic aside as he tries to stop you.

You move your Sten gun so it rests under your right arm where you will be able to fire it, if somewhat inaccurately with just one hand. As you jog back to the bridge you know you should be worried about snipers, but all you can think about is your men and the pain in your head.

Back under the bridge your men are pleased to see you. You check the explosives and see that the wire is still cut. Your men tell you that they fought off the last attack and are now waiting for another. As they speak you hear the unmistakeable sound of a tank rumbling down the road. You turn to see a Tiger tank with at least thirty German infantry trotting behind.

◊ *If you would like to try to retreat, go to 54.*
◊ *If you would like to send your men to safety and stay yourself to try to keep the explosives from the Germans, go to 28.*

---

12 *Sunday, 3:00 p.m. – 5 hours to sunset...*

You pass the order for your men to hide in the woods on either side of the road. You are impressed by how quickly the three sections rush into the nearby trees, blending into the undergrowth. You drop to your stomach and lie silently as the two German vehicles trundle past. At the front is an armoured car and you can clearly see the German soldier standing in the small turret, his arms resting on the heavy machine gun. Behind is a truck, which as it passes, you see is packed full of German soldiers.

You wait for a couple of minutes until the vehicles have disappeared to your right, before giving the order for your men to continue. They reappear from the woods and set off along the road that will lead to Arnhem Bridge.

◊ *Go to 95.*

Tuesday, morning...

The trip back to HQ is uneventful and you enter the house to find your men occupying the four rooms on the bottom floor. You check they are OK and talk briefly to Corporal Venables. You ask if Revie has appeared; he just shakes his head and looks away.

A few minutes later you are gazing from the window, wondering if 30 Corps will ever arrive. There has been a lull for the past thirty minutes and apart from distant thuds of mortar shells coming in from the Germans, all is quiet.

Major Tatham-Warter eventually comes to find you and stands next to you gazing out of the window. You can see the house you escaped from just across the street and are surprised when you spot a shadow moving. Your first thought is for Corporal Revie.

"We need to take it back," he says nodding in the direction of the destroyed platoon house. "The top two floors are unusable, but there have been reports that Germans are now inside."

You nod your head in agreement.

It takes just fifteen minutes to brief your men for the attack. Since Revie is missing and Ramsey is dead, you collect what remains of the three Sections – 14 men – into one Section with Corporal Venables in command.

The plan of attack is simple. Your two Bren guns will lay down fire from this building and the Section will assault the front door.

◊ *Go to 66.*

You pass the order to 1 and 2 Sections, together
with the two Brens, to deploy in the woods to the
left of the road. You instruct 3 Section to advance to
the crossroad, pass over the road and attack from
behind the Germans when the firing begins.

With your men in position, you watch the two
vehicles approach, with the armoured car in front.
When they are level you give the order to open
fire. 1 and 2 Sections put down a steady rate of fire,
their Lee Enfield rifles cracking out bullets which
smash windows of the truck and ping off the side
of the armoured car. You can hear the thump of the
machine guns as they open up too.

Before you can react, the armoured car begins
to turn around and then speeds past the truck and
back down the road.

The truck also begins to turn, but a burst of fire
from your men stops it dead.

You pass the word to stop firing. 3 Section
now emerge from the woods opposite and move
cautiously towards the back of the truck. By the
time you get down on to the road, about twenty
German soldiers are being led away.

Your men are excited after their first contact,
but you quickly calm them and order the advance
towards the bridge to continue.

◊ *Go to 95.*

Sunday, night...

The dark night conceals your movement and you warn your men to stay silent. You approach the wide stone staircase that zigzags up the grassy embankment and crouch down. Corporal Venables is at your side but for once he is quiet. You explain that you will lead the way and Venables and his ten men will follow.

You zigzag up the steps, keeping low and stop just before you get to the top, checking the safety on your Sten is off. Silently you scale the last few steps and creep onto the bridge.

Ahead of you is a wide road. It is two lanes across and could easily allow two cars to pass in either direction. A narrow pavement runs between the edge of the road and the bridge on each side. A low wall with an iron railing on top protects pedestrians from falling on each side of the road. The darkness makes it difficult to see too far, but you can just make out the two arches of the metal bridge. A cold breeze blows up from the river.

You signal for your men to follow you and start to advance on the right-hand side of the bridge. You keep low and silent as you edge forward. Suddenly you hear German voices in the dark and as you look across the bridge you see them. You signal your men to stop. You are virtually invisible in the darkness. A German officer is standing behind a truck, talking to a group of about fifteen German soldiers who are sitting inside.

◊ *If you wish to use the element of surprise and attack the truck, go to 37.*

◊ *If you wish to wait a moment and see what happens, go to 60.*

16 *Sunday, 7:45 p.m. – 15 minutes to sunset...*

You quickly decide to put down a base of fire on the armoured car, despite the fact the Lee Enfields will have little chance of penetrating the car's armour. You sprint forward to Corporal Venables, dropping to your knees behind the wall.

"You've picked a good day for a war," says Venables. "Shame Jerry is being a Peter party pooper."

You are about to reply when a stream of machine gun bullets sprays against the other side of the low wall. You both drop to the ground and are covered in dust and pieces of brick.

"Blimey!" he shouts.

You start to explain to Venables that you need his men to place down a base of fire, but realise it is pointless, since his men are pinned down.

You tell Venables that you are going to get help and then crawl away from the position. When you are a few paces away you crouch down and make your way back towards the underpass.

◊ *Go to 78.*

---

17 *Tuesday, morning...*

You wake early and head to the ground floor kitchen to find something to eat. You find a slice of bread, then head off to find Major Tatham-Warter.

The short journey through the streets is

dangerous. Twice shots ring out as you duck from doorway to doorway – you have no idea where the sniper is hiding.

Major Tatham-Warter is pleased to see you and quickly explains the situation. They have heard from 30 Corps, but they are still not over the river at Nijmegen. This means that the chances of them arriving today are zero. You also hear that it had been planned to drop some Polish paratroopers just the other side of the river, but this has also been delayed.

◊ *If you wish to return to your house by the same route, go to 64.*

◊ *If you wish to take a different route, go to 72.*

Tuesday, afternoon...

In the hours after Corporal Venables's death your men make themselves busy reinforcing the crumbling house, while you lack the energy to offer any real direction. However, when the shelling suddenly begins again you are sparked into life.

You make your way to the top floor and crouch down at the window that overlooks the street. You can see and hear artillery shells coming in all around you, thudding into the houses and showering debris. It is relentless, but for some reason you have no fear.

Suddenly the shelling stops. The light is fading when you hear the roar of a tank. At the end of the street you see the shape of a German Tiger tank. It stops as its turret smoothly swings the 88 mm gun towards your house.

You scream "TIGER!" as you bound out of the room and jump down the stairs. The first shell shakes the whole house.

◊ *To order your men into the cellar, go to 26.*

◊ *To get out of the house, go to 48.*

---

19 *Sunday, night...*

The streets are dark and silent following your attack on the bridge. 1 Section jog ahead of you, back to the house. Suddenly you hear a voice behind you. You spin around and see a man emerging from an alley. You are about to open fire when you spot his maroon beret. The paratrooper stumbles up to you – he is out of breath. He explains that the Major wishes to see you. You return to the bridge and find the Major.

◊ *Go to 55.*

---

20 *Sunday, night...*

The presence of Frost keeps your men's minds focused and progress from Oosterbeek is good. It is dark as you pass the sign for Arnhem and head into the town.

The Arnhem streets are deserted. You keep the river on your right-hand side and push on. Even with the gloom of the descending night you can make out the arches of the Arnhem road bridge. Frost is keen to keep your men moving and whenever you spot Germans he directs you off the main streets and through the gardens of houses and down back alleys. At one point you come across a group of about twenty German soldiers. Unseen by the enemy, Frost simply knocks on the door of a nearby house. It is opened by an old lady. Frost pushes past her and leads you through her house, out of the back door, through her back garden and down the next street.

You carefully navigate your way through the town's streets to within striking distance of the road bridge. Your men pick up the pace as they get closer.

◊ *Go to 30.*

Sunday, 7:30 p.m. – ½ hour to sunset...

You order 2 Section to spread out into an arrowhead formation and advance into the trees to the right. You tell 3 Section to form a line behind you and order 1 Section to guard the road.

You are quickly through the woods and emerge into a large, open valley. Ahead of you is a large river, which you assume is the Rhine, and a structure that you recognise as the Oosterbeek railway bridge. Dirty black smoke is rising from the centre of the bridge and the middle section has fallen away. You can see men on both sides of the broken bridge, exchanging gunfire.

Suddenly you hear a shout from behind. The tall figure of Major Tatham-Warter stumbles towards you through the long grass, his black umbrella waving high in the air. You stop and wait.

"Lieutenant," puffs the Major, "what are you up to?"

You begin to explain that you are giving support to the bridge attack.

"Are you a fool?" thunders the Major. "Are simple orders too much for you to understand?" He lifts his umbrella and points to the river that snakes away to your left. "The bridge we are heading for is in that direction. You are an idiot and I relieve you of your duties. Now return down the line and give yourself up to our Military Police."

You have no option but to trudge in shame back along the line. Though the operation continues, you are held in the custody of the Military Police.

◊ *Operation Market Garden is over for you. Go to 76 to discover your fate.*

Tuesday, morning... 22

Once back in the house you tell your platoon that 30 Corps are not expected today. You ask them to collect all their ammunition together and share it out equally. They scurry into action. You inspect the house's defences, making sure all the glass in the windows has been removed and furniture has been used to provide a makeshift barrier. You then wait in the top floor room for the Germans to come. You don't have to wait long.

The unmistakeable thunder of tanks on the move fills the air with dread. You peer out of the window into the street to the east just as three boxy Panzer Mark III tanks open fire on the house. The first shell fired slams into the wall a few metres away, throwing you to the floor. A second blasts the roof, filling the air with dust.

◊ *To order your men to use the PIAT to destroy the tanks, go to 71.*

◊ *If you wish to evacuate the building, go to 31.*

Wednesday, morning...

The number of Germans you have seen is making you nervous and you can feel a tension in the air. You give the order to retreat and within a couple of minutes your men are ready to move.

You set off north under the bridge. You pass the order to spread into an arrowhead formation. Within a few minutes you turn right onto the main road through the defended area. It is strewn with debris, and you can make out three burned-out metallic heaps that you assume are German tanks.

Your men slip into the HQ. You find the unknown Major on the top floor of the HQ, after a harrowing journey up the stairs past a huge number of injured men. You explain that the German presence is too strong and he simply nods.

"Well, it is just about over," he says looking at you. "Every man for himself I think." You nod in agreement.

You return downstairs, still shocked by the number of wounded paratroopers and pass the word to your men that they are to try and make their way to safety. They scurry about the injured men collecting ammunition and then share it out amongst the remains of the platoon. You shake the hand of each man in turn, and then send them off into the streets to try and find their way to safety. You wait a few minutes and follow your men,

praying that you will be able to make it past
enemy lines…

◊ *You have fought hard and commanded your men well
– this is the end of the Battle of Arnhem for you. Go
to 36 to discover what happened in the real battle.*

Monday, afternoon...
Soon it is late afternoon and your thoughts return
to 30 Corps. They should have arrived by now, and
without their support the situation is becoming
desperate. Your men are low on ammunition,
though they seem ready to carry on fighting.

As the afternoon drags on you hear fighting
to the east. You consider going to see what is
happening, but German snipers have made
movement in the streets almost impossible.
Instead, you warn your platoon to be ready for
another German attack. It is only as the light fades
that an artillery bombardment begins. At first it is
just a few mortar rounds and tank shells that slam
into the nearby houses. However, as the night falls,
more German shells rain down.

You ask for a few volunteers to remain in the
top rooms and send the rest of the men to the
safety of the basement.

◊ *To remain in the top room during the bombardment,
go to 87.*

◊ *If you wish to seek shelter in the cellar, go to 51.*

25 *Tuesday, morning...*

You sternly tell Frank that the tank will have retreated back to his own lines and this is the way to go. He shrugs and you set off once again, turning left. Ahead the road splits into two, with a narrow street heading towards the river and the wide road continuing east.

You walk cautiously towards this junction, with Frank a few paces behind. As you cross the road spurts of dust appear at your feet, followed by the rattle of gunfire. Frank throws himself left, rolling into a nearby doorway. You turn – a popping sound fills your ears. You slump to the floor. In your final moments, you can see Captain Frank cowering in the safety of a nearby doorway, his arm outstretched, words you will never hear moving on his lips.

◊ *You have been killed in action. Go to 68 to discover your fate.*

---

26 *Tuesday, afternoon...*

You order your men into the cellar. You stand by the door; as the paratroopers push past, you urge them to move faster. When you are sure everyone is down you follow them.

You crouch with your men in the cold cellar for at least an hour listening to the shells impacting above you. When you finally emerge you creep to the second floor and look out of the window. The Tiger has gone.

Your men reposition themselves in the house and word comes to you that the defences are holding. You tell the men to prepare for another attack, but none comes. The night is now closing in and as the darkness falls you see the figure of a British soldier ducking into your house. He is a paratrooper and explains that Lt. Col. Frost and Major Tatham-Warter are both injured and out of action. He instructs you to stay here overnight and make your way to HQ in the morning.

The paratrooper disappears back into the darkness. Many houses are now burning – you can hear the roar and crackle of flame all around you. Occasionally you can hear the distant irregular dong of a church bell. You do not sleep well.
◊   *Go to 98.*

Sunday, night...

You send 1 Section back to the house and head into the darkness to find Major Tatham-Warter. He is standing under the same bridge section and is surrounded by a group of paratroopers. They are all huddled over a map, illuminated by the Major's small torch. As you approach, the Major looks up.

"Ah, just the man."
◊   *Go to 55.*

28 *Wednesday, morning...*

You think quickly. The tank and infantry are still a hundred metres away and your men have a chance to get away. You turn to them and order them to retreat. You tell them to go to the HQ and bring reinforcements, if possible. They begin to complain, but when they see you are serious they turn and break into a run.

You crouch behind the nearest concrete pillar, reload your Sten gun and then position your good hand so it can fire. If you can keep the tank at bay then maybe your men can get back before the Germans blow the bridge.

You do not wait until the Germans are within range before sending a burst of gunfire over their heads. You smile as the troops drop to the ground. You would wait to fire the second burst knowing it will give away your position but the tank keeps coming. You have no choice but to squeeze the trigger and watch as the bullets ricochet off the front of the tank.

To your surprise the tank stops and for a moment you think you might have had a lucky hit. However, the turret twists, rotating the muzzle of cannon in your direction. The ground rocks with the force of the shell as it explodes in front of you, blowing you off you feet. You roll away, wincing with pain. You stagger to your feet, Sten gun at

your hip, and squeeze the trigger and do not let go. As the bullets shudder from the gun you start to sprint towards the tank, sparks flying off the armour as they hit.

A bullet from a well-aimed German rifle catches you in the neck – spraying blood all over you. You drop down dead.

◊ *You have died fighting to hold the bridge until the last moment. The Battle of Arnhem is over for you. Go to 49 to discover about Lieutenant Grayburn.*

---

29 *Sunday, 3:30 p.m. – 4 ½ hours to sunset...*

You quickly pass the order not to fire and tell Corporal Revie to capture the German. He barks orders to the nearest men and three of them sprint up the road after the bike.

The following moments are like a scene from a comedy film. The paratroopers call directions to each other as they run, while the German continues to wobble along the road. As your men get close, the German's wobbling becomes so extreme that he finally loses balance lands on his backside. A chorus of laughs rises from your men as the soldiers from 1 Section capture the German.

You speak to the German prisoner. He is about 50 years old and looks scared. His English is OK and he is eager to tell you that a company of elite SS troops are based in Arnhem.

You are eager to move on and order the prisoner to be taken down the line. You drop 1 Section behind and move 2 Section to the front. Their leader is Corporal Venables, a jolly Londoner who you have shared a few drinks with over time. He positions his men in an arrowhead formation before you once again begin the advance.

◊ *Go to 34.*

30

Sunday, night...

The bridge looms out of the darkness. You are approaching it from a side street surrounded by high town houses. Thick concrete columns support the main road to the bridge high above your head. You quicken your pace and look across to Frost just as a shot rings out and he is thrown backwards.

You shout "SNIPER!" and drop onto the cobbled street. Your men follow your example – then a storm of gunfire erupts. It seems that every window in every house has a German gun firing at you. Bullets rip into the ground. You try to get to your feet but a bullet nicks the muscle of your left leg, throwing you to the ground. You turn, shouting "MEDIC!", only to see Corporal Venables as he is struck in the chest. He slumps over. His men panic and scramble for cover.

The German gunfire continues. You push your face into the cold cobbles and pray.

Eventually the firing stops and all you can hear are the groans of your men. You slowly lift your head to see eight or nine men lying close by – all paratroopers, all dead. You slowly pull yourself up, your leg throbbing in pain. Out of the gloom emerge a number of Germans pointing guns straight at you. You lift your arms in surrender.

◊ *You have been captured and are now a prisoner of war. Go to 76 to discover your fate.*

Tuesday, morning...

You scramble from the floor, brush the dust from your face and scream for your platoon to get out of the house. You sprint from the room and onto the landing, again screaming for your men to get out. You are thundering down the stairs when another shell hits and you are thrown down; only a quick grasp of the banister saves you from a nasty fall. From the sound behind you, you guess that about seven or eight men are following you.

When you reach the bottom Corporal Revie is standing at the door instructing the paratroopers to get out and to head towards the buildings opposite. You duck past Revie and tell him to follow. He flashes a salute and you are away. You run across the street, head down. You hear another shell hit and swing around to see your men streaming from the house.

The house opposite is occupied by British soldiers you don't recognise. You ignore them as you watch the upper east side of the house you have just evacuated start to crumble and fall. The tanks finally stop shelling and disappear from view. You locate Venables and a quick word shows you have lost five men. There is no sign of Corporal Revie.

◊   *Go to 89.*

32

Monday, morning...

Though the bridge is blocked, German soldiers jump down from three half-tracks. They are coming under a lot of gunfire from all directions. You take another PIAT bomb and carefully place it into the front of the PIAT tube. You glance through the sights, aiming at the nearest half-track, and pull the trigger. The projectile pops from the PIAT. This time your aim is better and the projectile explodes against the half-track. Sooty black smoke billows from the wreckage.

The remaining Germans are running back across the bridge. You decide to save ammunition and watch as they disappear from view.

An eerie silence returns to the bridge. The road is now blocked by burning and disabled vehicles, and littered with dead and dying Germans.

You look away from the scene as your training kicks in. You send Corporal Venables to see if you have any casualties and tell him to warn the men to be ready for another attack. He disappears and returns shortly to say that no one is injured. The men in your room relax and you take the chance to walk around the house, going room to room, speaking to your men.

◊   *Go to 24.*

Sunday, night...
Having the Major breathing down your neck is one thing, but a Lt. Col. is just too much. You turn to Frost and explain that you are the kind of leader who needs room, and you would be grateful if he didn't tag along with your platoon. Frost turns in your direction and you notice that he is going a strange colour of purple.

"The day I take orders from a Lieutenant," booms Frost, spittle collecting on his hairy lip, "is the day I give it all up and join the Bosch." It looks as though Lt. Col. Frost will be coming along.
◊ *Go to 20.*

Sunday, 4:00 p.m. - 4 hours to sunset...
You push along the road again as it enters a wood and, despite the chance of an ambush, 2 Section move quickly. However, it is not long before the trees once again start to thin out.

A few paces ahead, Corporal Venables suddenly stops, his left hand raised in the "halt" signal. You duck over to Venables.

"Up ahead – I thought I saw something," he whispers.

You strain your eyes but cannot see anything. Major Tatham-Warter walks up behind you, but before you can speak to him the rattle of machine gun fire echoes from ahead. 2 Section return fire.

The gunfire is coming from a small clump of trees over to the left of the road. As you assess the situation a shell explodes just in front of your position. Instinctively you drop to the ground and a shower of soil patters onto your back and maroon beret. A second mortar shell explodes over to your right. You must act now!

◊ *To move your platoon into a defensive position, lay down suppressive fire and attempt to force the Germans to retreat from the trees, go to 82.*

◊ *To order an attack on the German position, go to 73.*

---

35 *Tuesday, morning...*

Before you can say anything, the Major smiles. "Good man. I knew I could count on you," he says looking at you. It seems you don't really have a choice. The Major turns sharply and strides into the next room, where he is quickly deep in conversation with a Lieutenant. Captain Frank steps forward and shakes your hand.

"Look," he says in a deep Liverpudlian accent. "All you need to do is carry this." He thrusts a khaki-coloured bag into your hands containing about ten PIAT bombs.

"Oh, and don't get killed."

You smile, but before you can answer Frank is ducking out of the door. You sling the bag over your shoulder and follow. You find Frank pressed against the wall of a house at the end of the street. To your left you can see the destroyed platoon house but there is no sign of the tanks.

"Which way?" asks Frank.

◊ *To head north past the destroyed platoon house, go to 3.*

◊ *If you wish to head east away from the house but towards the German line, go to 99.*

What really happened?

Approximately 6,800 Allied troops were captured during the Battle of Arnhem, 4,000 escaped or were evacuated, and just under 2,000 were killed in action. German losses totalled around 1,300 men.

The real Battle of Arnhem did see John Frost and his men capture Arnhem Bridge, but they were unable to hold it for long. The rest of the British paratroopers became caught up in a battle with the Germans in Arnhem town and were later evacuated across the river to safety.

The Polish paratroopers arrived too late and were unable to help the British on the bridge. Yet perhaps most disappointing was the fact that the tanks of 30 Corps stopped a few kilometres from Arnhem. It was thought to be too dangerous for them to advance onto the bridge, leaving John Frost and his men to fight for their lives.

John Frost was injured whilst defending the bridge and was captured by the Germans. He spent the remainder of the war in a German hospital. After the war he remained in the army. In 1978 the bridge over the Rhine at Arnhem was renamed the John Frost Bridge.

Digby Tatham-Warter did teach his men to use bugle calls. He also carried an umbrella, using it as a method of identification in battle, saying only a "bloody fool of an Englishman" would be seen in combat with an umbrella. Tatham-Warter and his men were some of the last British soldiers on the bridge. His final radio message was "out of ammo, God save the King". He surrendered minutes later. Tatham-Warter was in the same German hospital as Frost, but escaped. He spent the final months of the war disguised as a deaf mute, riding a bicycle around the Dutch countryside, helping Allied prisoners who had escaped from the Germans.

37

Sunday, night...

You turn to Corporal Venables and pass the instruction to attack the truck. The whispered order passes to the ten men who are crouching in the dark behind you. You hiss a slow 1...2...3...

You pull the trigger on your Sten gun, shattering the silence as you and 2 Section riddle the truck with bullets. The German officer is cut down – German voices scream from inside the truck.

Then the truck starts to move, heading back

towards the safety of the German side. You and your men follow for a few steps, but the truck quickly disappears into the darkness.

Corporal Venables steps forward to examine the dead German officer. He never makes it. A stream of bullets throws him backwards. You crouch down, scanning the gloom of the bridge, before you see the square concrete pillbox about 10 metres away. Through the narrow slot of blackness a machine gun muzzle spits fire again.

You jump up, turn and run – screaming for your men to retreat. You take just three steps before bullets thud into your back, tearing the life from your body.

◊ *You succeeded in reaching Arnhem, but have made the ultimate sacrifice. Go to 76 to discover your fate.*

Sunday, night...

Slowly you are able to work your way back to Major Tatham-Warter, without exposing yourself to the machine gunner. The Major is standing just outside the three houses near the underpass. Beside him is Lt. Col. John Frost the battalion commander. Frost sports a magnificently bushy moustache, shrugged shoulders and seems small next to the lanky Major.

You explain the situation ahead. Frost listens, carefully stroking his moustache as you speak.

When you have finished he thanks you and turns to B Company commander Major Crawley who is standing close by. Frost simply points in the direction of the German machine gun and says, "Deal with it." Crawley salutes and heads off.

The German machine gun continues to splutter and spit for about 15 minutes before gunfire breaks out to your left.

"OK, let's get moving," orders Frost. It seems Frost will be joining your advance. You pause for a moment unsure what to do next.

◊ *If you feel uncomfortable with the battalion commander at your side, go to 33.*
◊ *If you wish to do as he orders, go to 20.*

---

39 *Sunday, 7:45 p.m. – 15 minutes to sunset...*
You know you must push on to Arnhem, so you ignore the smoke. The streets on the outskirts of Oosterbeek are deserted. Ahead there is a narrow tunnel which cuts under the railway. 2 Section are the first through when suddenly you hear the thunder of German machine gun fire, and the cries of injured men.

You sprint into the short tunnel, Sten gun at the ready. You can hear the cracking echoes of the Lee Enfields coming from the other side of the darkness. The light brings horror. About 200 metres ahead you can see a German armoured car sitting at a bend in the road, its machine gun spitting fire. Just ahead of you is a dead paratrooper from 2 Section, a second man lies in the undergrowth clutching his own mangled hand. To your right Corporal Venables has ducked behind a low wall, directing the rest of his men to fire on the armoured car.

◊ *If you wish to pass the order for the 6-pounder anti-tank gun to be brought up, go to 78.*

◊ *If you wish to pull 2 Section back and go on the defensive, go to 16.*

Sunday, 7 p.m. – 1 hour to sunset...

You sprint back through the underpass and give the order for the 6-pounder to be brought forward. You then tell Corporal Revie of 1 Section and Corporal Ramsey of 3 Section to get their men forward and to put suppressing fire down on the armoured car.

You return through the underpass and arrive to find Corporal Venables standing in the middle of the road, over the body of a dead private. There is no sign of the armoured car.

"He's legged it!" Venables says, pointing around the bend.

The casualties are removed and then you order all three Sections to advance. You send 2 Section along the road, 1 Section spreads out to the left and 3 Section heads off behind the houses on your right. As you round the bend bullets rake the road.

You throw yourself to the ground, rolling into bushes at the side of the road. You crawl forward to a low brick wall. This time it is not the armoured car – it's a machine gun up on a mound to the left.

Your men hide behind any cover they can. The German gunner is accurate, whenever they move he produces a burst of fire – you are pinned down.

◊ *If you wish to order an attack, go to 83.*

◊ *If you wish to see what Major Tatham-Warter wishes you to do, go to 6.*

It is daylight when you are woken by another explosion. You rush to the hole in the wall that was made the night before. The pillbox is charred black and all of the wooden huts are just ash. The metal arches are also burned black. In the centre of the bridge there are three burned-out trucks. There is another small explosion towards the south end of the bridge, followed by another, then silence.

Ten minutes later Corporal Revie appears with a hunk of bread and a large slice of yellow cheese. You thank him and tuck in.

"The Jerries tried breaking through out east during the night," Revie says. "But I heard that the B Company boys knocked out a German tank. How about that!"

You smile at the news and say that you expect 30 Corps to appear today. You tell him they are fighting from the south and will be coming over the bridge from the other end.

The next hour is spent reinforcing the top floor defences. You order 2 Section and Corporal Venables's men to join you, since the top room offers a great defence position. A Bren gun is set up in the rubble next to the hole in the wall, and the remainder of the men find good places from which to fire onto the bridge. You order that a PIAT be brought up and after about 20 minutes a man from

2 Section appears with a PIAT and ammunition.

Suddenly you hear a shout from the other side of the house. You look out onto the bridge where there are a number of vehicles on the south side.

"It's 30 Corps," says Venables. "Oh the lovely, lovely men – I always did like the Staffs." Venables then starts a little jig, slapping his hands on his thighs as he dances and sings a rather rude song.

You fumble for your binoculars and home in on the vehicles as they start to cross the bridge. They are German! You shout for the man to prepare to repel the attack. Venables stops dancing and instead swears loudly.

◊ *To fire the Bren machine gun, go to 62.*
◊ *To direct the firing of the PIAT anti-tank gun, go to 5.*

---

42 *Sunday, 7 p.m. – 1 hour to sunset...*

You pass orders for 2 Section to spread out into an arrowhead formation to the right; 3 Section to form a line behind you and for 1 Section to guard the road. You head towards the smoke and the Oosterbeek railway bridge.

You make rapid progress, despite the close attention of a herd of black and white cows, when you suddenly hear a shout from behind. Turning, you see the tall figure of Major Tatham-Warter. He is stumbling through the long grass, his black umbrella waving high in the air. You stop and wait.

"Lieutenant," puffs the Major as he nears your position. "What are you up to?" You begin to explain that you are giving support to the bridge attack.

"Are you a fool?" thunders the Major. "Are simple orders too much for you to comprehend? You are an idiot, and I relieve you of your duties. Now return down the line and give yourself up to our MPs."

◊ *You have no option but to hand yourself over to the Military Police. Operation Market Garden is over for you. Go to 76 to discover your fate.*

Monday, morning...

The German soldiers move to take up positions on the bridge, but they come under heavy gunfire. You aim at the half-tracks and squeeze the trigger. The gun jerks, releasing a few bullets then stops. You are out of ammo! You snatch out the curved magazine that thrusts from the top of the gun and replace it with a full one. Looking back down the sights you can see that vehicles have not moved. You squeeze the trigger again, sending a shower of sparks off the armour of the nearest half-track. Most of the infantry have now retreated along the bridge and you stop firing.

An eerie silence returns to the bridge. The road is blocked by burning and disabled vehicles.

Among them lie the bodies of German soldiers.

Your training kicks in. You send Corporal Venables off to see if you have any casualties and tell him to warn the men to be ready for another attack. He disappears and returns shortly to say that no one is injured. The men in your room relax and you take the chance to walk around the house, going room to room, speaking to your men.

◊ *Go to 24.*

---

44 *Wednesday, morning...*

You realise that there is nothing more to be done here. You shake MacKay by the hand, wish him good luck, and order your troops back out of the window through which they came. You jog down the stairs avoiding the books and papers and dodge into the small back room.

You are the last out of the window and your men are all hiding in the thick undergrowth on the other side of the window. The fire is now burning fiercely and you can feel the heat coming from the roof. Suddenly a huge explosion rips up the soft earth a couple of metres from your position.

"Incoming mortar," a voice screams.

Your men instinctively scatter, trying to get as far away as possible from any other shells. You decide to make a run for it across the grassy area. You start sprinting, moving past the recently created crater. Suddenly you see a German tank in the road a few metres ahead. You veer to the left and take a few paces only to see four Germans appear through the undergrowth.

You feel very tired and simply stop in the middle of the grass. You glance to the tank on your right and the men in front and decide it is time to surrender. You slowly lift your hands above you head, letting your Sten drop to the ground. The nearest soldier looks no more than eighteen years old and he is carrying a small sub-machine-gun. You are shocked to see him raise the gun in your direction. He pulls the trigger. The bullets rack across your body. You are dead before you hit the ground.

◊ *You have fought hard and commanded your men well – this is the end of the Battle of Arnhem for you. Now go to 36 to discover what happened in the real battle.*

45 *Tuesday, morning...*

You peek around the corner and see the tank about 40 metres away. It is sitting in the middle of the street, its engine chugging slowly. The house on the opposite side of the road has a low garden wall in front, though it is blackened and mostly rubble – it will be a good place to fire the PIAT.

Frank jams the PIAT between his feet, twists and pulls until it clicks. He then peeks around the corner before sprinting across the road and kneeling behind the low wall. You wait, watching.

"Ammo," he hisses.

Suddenly you remember and dart forward, pulling a PIAT projectile from your bag as you run across the road. You dive over the low wall next to Frank. Carefully you drop the projectile into the loading slot. You tap Frank on the helmet to indicate it is loaded. You wait a moment and then there is a pop and the projectile fizzes across the street slamming into the rear of the tank. There is a small explosion – and the engine grinds to a stop.

You wait five minutes until deciding the tank is definitely out of action. Then you creep to the top of the street and stare past the disabled tank. The road runs east with the river on the left and houses to the right. You see no other tanks and decide to return to HQ.

◊ *Go to 13.*

Sunday, 2:30 p.m. – 5 ½ hours to sunset...

You arrive at the rendezvous to learn that your platoon have all landed safely. You walk amongst your men reminding them that they are now in enemy territory and they need to be ready for action. After just a few minutes Major Digby Tatham-Warter, your commanding officer, calls you over. His tall, thin body makes his rough, khaki battledress look baggy. Yet, the most unusual thing about the Major is that he is holding a black rolled-up umbrella.

"Lt. Col. Frost has asked that A Company head the advance along Lion Route." As he speaks he adjusts the maroon beret that marks him out as a

paratrooper. "Our job is to get to Arnhem Bridge as fast as possible. We have the element of surprise over the Jerries, but we must move quickly. Lion Route will take us along the river and right into Arnhem. We are not expecting too much trouble. Your boys of 4 Platoon will take lead point. Just keep to the road, and whatever happens, keep moving. We must be on the bridge by sunset." The Major salutes and turns away before you can reply.

You return to your platoon and within a couple of minutes you are on the move. You send out 1 Section ahead, ordering them to advance in an arrowhead formation. 2 Section and 3 Section are ordered to the left and right.

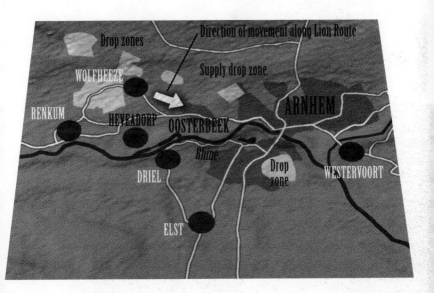

You cross the ploughed fields heading south and join the narrow road leading to Arnhem – about 8 kilometres away. At first the road cuts through open fields. Your men stay in formation and make good progress. Soon the road threads into a wood.

The woods are strangely quiet, but the trees are well spaced and you can see into the undergrowth ahead. No one speaks as your men pick their way along the road. Ahead you can see a crossroads, where a larger road cuts across the road you are on. Suddenly Corporal Revie of 1 Section stops. He is a small man with a face that looks like it has been chipped out of stone, but a good soldier. His left hand is raised above his shoulder, his fist clenched. Your platoon sees the signal to halt and drops into a crouch.

You move forward and the Corporal silently points towards the crossroads. In the distance, coming down the road on the left, you can see a German truck and an armoured car.

◊ *To set up an ambush and attack the vehicles, go to 61.*
◊ *To hide and let the Germans pass, go to 12.*

---

47 *Wednesday, morning...*
You give the order to lay down fire. Your men fan out across the road. Tall houses on the left-hand side have been reduced to rubble, with one still burning. The river runs along on the right,

although a line of trees offers some cover. Two men quickly set up the Bren gun in the centre of the road, whilst you skip to the left. The Germans are about 50 metres ahead of you and they are unaware of your presence until the firing begins.

You are the first to fire, taking aim with your Sten before pulling the trigger. You squeeze off a few shots before the cracks of your platoon's Lee Enfields start. One German drops to the ground. The other Germans scatter. Then the Bren kicks into action. A few splutters of gunfire drop another German before they all disappear from view.

You order your men forward and quickly arrive under the bridge. You order your troops to set up a defensive perimeter, whilst you cut the wire to the explosives.

◊ *If you now wish to return to the HQ, go to 23.*
◊ *If you want to wait to make sure the Germans do not return, go to 8.*

48 *Tuesday, afternoon...*

As you bound down the stairs you give the order to evacuate the house. You stand by the door pushing the paratroopers into the street as they appear. When you are sure everyone is out, you turn to leave. A second shell slams into the house sending rubble and dust tumbling into the hall. You put your hand onto the doorway to stop yourself falling and then spring into the street.

The cobbled street is covered with debris. You look up to see your men safely entering the house opposite. You glance to your left and see the Tiger tank blocking the road about 100 metres away. The main gun is thrust high, but the tank's machine gun swivels at the front of the beast.

The impact of the bullets lifts you off your feet as you are cut down.

◊ *You have died in the line of duty. Go to 68 to discover your fate.*

---

49 The Victoria Cross medal is the highest award for bravery that can be given to a solider. There were five VCs awarded during the Battle of Arnhem, one was to Lieutenant Jack Grayburn.

In the later stages of the battle, the Germans set their sights on demolishing part of the bridge. To do this they placed explosives on the archways. A group of British paratroopers, led by Lieutenant

Donald Hindley set out under heavy German gunfire to remove the charges. Hindley explains that they were "working a few metres away from a large quantity of explosives which could be fired at any moment".

Despite already being injured, Grayburn was part of this group. After successfully defusing the explosives, Grayburn was wounded again by German gunfire. He was treated by medics and insisted that he be allowed to continue in the battle. He returned to fight with one arm in a sling and a bandage on his head.

When it became clear that the Germans had reset the fuses, Grayburn and his men returned for a second time. However, the Germans were prepared and had moved up a tank to cover the explosives. In full view of the enemy, Grayburn directed the withdrawal of the British paratroopers. He was killed later that night, falling into the Rhine after he was shot. His body remained lost to the river for a number of years and was not found until 1948.

The Victoria Cross was awarded posthumously (after his death).

◊ *Now go to 36 to discover what happened in the real battle.*

Sunday, 6 p.m. – 2 hours to sunset...

Your men quickly recover from the attack and within a few minutes you are moving along Lion Route again. At the head of the column in an arrowhead formation is 2 Section. The other Sections are positioned behind you on the road.

It is not long before you can see a village to your right, and word comes down the line that it is Heveadorp. You push on past, aware that you must reach Arnhem before sunset. Eventually, the trees give way to square orange-roofed houses, and you see a sign for Oosterbeek – Arnhem is still 7 kilometres away.

You pass the word for your men to be on the lookout for Germans as you enter the town. However, it seems that your arrival is no secret. Despite the fact you enter from a side road, the town's streets are filled with people. They cheer as you try to pass. The people swarm around your men, many carrying orange flags and pushing food and drink into your hands. At one point a pretty young girl runs up and kisses your cheek, thanking you in Dutch. Your men chuckle as your face blushes red. Soon it becomes difficult to move on at any speed.

◊ *To pass the order for your men to ignore the crowds and push onwards, go to 53.*

◊ *To let your men enjoy the moment, go to 77.*

51 *Monday, night...*

You leave two men from 3 Section in the top room and head to the basement. Most of the platoon are crammed into the small space and there is little noise as they try to sleep. Revie and Venables are playing cards under the light of a candle.

"Fancy a game?" asks Venables as you tiptoe into the room. You shake your head and instead find a small space in the corner of the basement. Here you curl up into a ball to get some sleep.

◊ *Go to 17.*

---

52 *Wednesday, morning...*

You awake with a headache. Your left arm is throbbing. It takes you a few minutes to realise that you are in the crowded treatment room on the bottom floor of the HQ. You start to rise, but a medic gently puts his hand on your shoulder.

"Easy," he says in a soft voice. "You have taken a bullet to the arm, and caught a bit of shrapnel in the head for good measure. You need to rest."

You look down at your damaged arm and put your hand up to your head to feel a bandage. You ask how long you have been here. The medic glances at his watch.

"Hmmmm… 30 minutes?"

◊ *If you wish to stay and rest, go to 92.*

◊ *If you wish to try and return to your men, go to 11.*

Sunday, 6:30 p.m. – 1 ½ hours to sunset...

You find Corporal Venables in the crowd. His round face beams at you and you can see red lipstick on his cheek mixing in with the black camouflage paint. You order Venables to get his men moving, reminding him that you are fighting a war. He smiles and pushes back through the crowd. You hear him screaming at his men to get moving and within a few minutes you are once again pushing forward.

You skirt around the centre of the town keeping the river to your right. The crowds quickly thin out. After marching on for about 10 minutes you hear a dull thud in the distance to your right. Looking out over the trees you can see smoke rising from the railway bridge that spans the river just south of Oosterbeek.

◊ *If you wish to leave Lion Route and find out what has happened, go to 42.*

◊ *If you wish to follow your orders and advance along Lion Route, go to 90.*

Wednesday, morning...

You scream the order to retreat and point in the opposite direction to the tank. You start running along the river road.

You are tired and your pace quickly slows. You glance over your shoulder to see your men have caught up with you and the Germans are not following. You eventually veer over to the riverbank and stop running. You place your gun on the ground and bend over to catch your breath.

"Sir, I think you should see this," says a voice.

You look up to see one of your men pointing to the road ahead. You slowly move your head in the direction of his outstretched finger. Standing in the road, just metres away, are about fifteen German soldiers. They have their rifles raised and pointed directly at your men. You slowly lift your hands into the air and have no choice but to surrender.

◊ *You have fought hard and commanded your men well – this is the end of the Battle of Arnhem for you. Now go to 36 to discover what happened in the real battle.*

---

55 *Sunday, night...*

Major Tatham-Warter talks confidently, his umbrella firmly clutched in his right hand.

"I want you to lead another attack, old boy," he says, pointing the black umbrella in your direction. "Take your platoon and knock out that darned machine gun."

Realising that this is all the direction you are going to get, you salute the Major and call your three Corporals to your side. You explain that you intend to attack along the bridge with all three sections. 1 Section will cross the bridge road and

attack on the left. 2 Section will advance along
the road and lay down suppressing fire, whilst
3 Section will attack from the right.

Within ten minutes your men are scrambling
up the grassy embankment. You tag onto 3 Section.
The darkness hides your men, but also makes it
difficult to see the pillbox. You are behind 1 Section
and 2 Section when your men are spotted.

From the right you see the muzzle of the
German machine gun, safe in its concrete bunker,
firing on your advancing men. 3 Section are within
touching distance of the concrete pillbox and stand
no chance. As you pull on the trigger of your Sten,
sending bullets uselessly towards the pillbox, you
watch helplessly as the men from 3 Section begin
to die. Three paratroopers slump to the ground like
rag dolls. A fourth turns and starts to run; you see
that it is Corporal Ramsey. As his arms and legs
pump, his maroon beret slips from his head. He
pauses to pick it up, only to be gunned down.

◊ *If you wish to order a retreat, go to 4.*
◊ *If you wish to order 1 Section and 2 Section to*
   attack, go to 91.

Sunday, 7 p.m. – 1 hour to sunset...   **56**
Your men quickly recover from the encounter
and are soon back on the move again. 2 Section
led by Venables lead the column in an arrowhead

formation, while the other Sections are lined up behind you on the road. The paratroopers are worried about being attacked but you urge your men to pick up the pace.

It is not long before you can see a village to your right and the word comes down the line that it is Heveadorp. You decide to ignore the village and push on. Eventually you see a sign for Oosterbeek.

As you enter the town you pass the word for your men to be on the lookout for Germans. But it looks like they have already cleared out – the town's roads are lined with Dutch people cheering as you try to pass. They swarm around your men, pushing food and drink into their hands. At one point a pretty young girl runs up and plants a huge kiss on your cheek, thanking you in Dutch. Your men chuckle as your face blushes red.

At first you are pleased by the crowds, but it quickly becomes difficult to move on at any speed.

◊ *To pass the order for your men to push on, go to 100.*
◊ *To let your men enjoy the moment, go to 77.*

---

57 *Wednesday, morning...*

You ignore the tank on the hill and order your men to cross the grassy area as quickly as possible. You all race forward at a sprint, ducking under low hanging branches and manoeuvring around small bushes. As you run you hear a few shots ring off in the distance, but you just keep your head down.

The school is a square, three-story building with a tiled roof and small rectangular windows. Or it was before the Germans started. It is now a wreck with huge shell holes throughout the top two storeys. As you stop and look up you can see black smoke starting to billow from under the roof.

You direct your men in through a ground-floor window. Inside there are books, desks and papers scattered everywhere. You head up the first set of narrow stairs that you find. You can now clearly smell acrid smoke and you are met on the stairs by a man you recognise from 1st Parachute squadron; it is Eric MacKay. He is a plain looking man and is shocked to see you in the school. You quickly explain that you have come to help get the injured paratroopers to safety. He smiles.

"Afraid you're too late, Old Boy," says the Captain. "The fire has taken hold. I have just ordered the men to get out." You ask what is happening to the wounded. "Most are already out of the cellar. The walking wounded are being left to surrender upstairs."

◊ *To stay with the wounded and make sure they are treated well by the Germans, go to 79.*

◊ *To try to make it back to the HQ, go to 44.*

58 *Sunday, night...*

The two paratroopers push into the room and lay
their weapons on the floor, before peering through
the window to the bridge beyond. They mutter
between themselves and suspiciously eye the
wall of the room. You step forward and explain
that you have no intention of letting them destroy
the house.

"Well, Sir," says the Geordie, "you can go and
ask the Major yourself. But the problem is that the
second you leave this room we are going to blow
a bloody big hole in that wall." As he speaks he
points to the wall. You pause, considering your
options and then just tell them to get on with it.
◊ *Go to 86.*

59 *Sunday, 2 p.m. – 6 hours to sunset...*

You sling your Sten sub-machine-gun over your
shoulder and head off towards the smoke. The
field is soft and looks as though it has been
recently ploughed. You occasionally slip in the
mud, but manage not to fall. Soldiers scurry about
in groups of two or three, all darting in different
directions. Discarded parachutes flap in the breeze.
You spot the familiar figure of the tall, thin frame
of Brigadier "Legs" Lathbury. As he walks in your
direction you stop, straighten your back and flash
a salute.

"Where are you going, paratrooper?" he thunders. You begin to stammer and explain, but the Brigadier cuts you short. "Second Battalion is in that direction," he says pointing to the east, already striding away. You pause, and then march off in the direction he pointed, feeling very much like a lost puppy.

◊ *Go to 46.*

Sunday, night...

After just a few minutes the German officer stops speaking to the men in the back of the truck and climbs into the cab. The engine chugs to life and the truck heads south back towards the German side of the river.

The air becomes filled with the choking fumes of the truck and you wait a few minutes before edging forward once again. In the night's darkness you can make out the shapes of small buildings or huts. There seems to be four or five. You can also see figures moving in the gloom.

A shot rings out and a German soldier appears immediately in front of you. Instinctively you squeeze the trigger of your gun and a burst of bullets hits him in the chest and throws him to the ground. Suddenly you can see a mass of shadowy shapes emerging from the darkness.

You have little choice but to signal the order to

retreat. You hear Venables screaming to his men to get moving and suddenly you are all sprinting back the way you came. Bullets whizz past your ears. You are breathing hard, your lungs gasping for air. The steps from the bridge appear on your left, and you bound down them to the bottom.

You are checking that 1 Section are uninjured, when Major Tatham-Warter appears – his face concerned, his umbrella grasped in this right hand. You explain that the bridge is well defended. The Major thanks you and disappears back under the bridge. You order 1 Section back to the house.

◊ *If you wish to return to your house, go to 19.*

◊ *If you wish to find the Major and give him more details about the troops on the bridge, go to 27.*

---

61 *Sunday, 3:00 p.m. – 5 hours to sunset...*

You have two options for the ambush of the armoured car and truck. You could opt for an all-out attack, which would see your men charging from the trees surrounding the crossroad and overwhelming the vehicles. Or, the alternative is to set up a flanking attack. This would see 1 Section and 2 Section setting up position in the woods where you are now, with 3 Section crossing the road to your right and attacking from the side.

◊ *To order an all-out attack, go to 97.*

◊ *To order a flanking attack, go to 14.*

ALL-OUT ATTACK

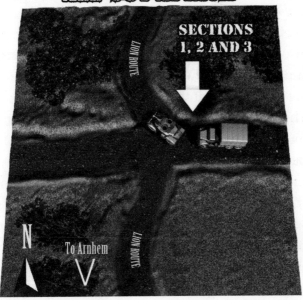

FLANKING ATTACK

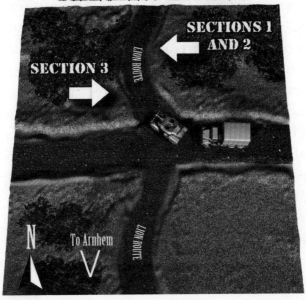

Monday, morning...

The German vehicles speed onto the bridge, weaving past the burned-out trucks and pushing along the road. At the front are motorcycles, followed by about twenty armoured cars and behind these are half-tracks packed full of German troops. You are surprised to see British artillery shells dropping onto the bridge. They are accurate – destroying the motorcycles, but have little effect on the armoured vehicles. The house is almost level with the bridge road and the German vehicles are no more than 100 metres away. You wait until the first few armoured cars are level before you open fire.

Gunfire comes in from all directions, and not just your house. Rifles, machine guns and anti-tank weapons all unleash death onto the bridge. The lead armoured car is hit first and the second rams into it from behind, blocking the road.

You are lying on the floor with the machine gun pointing out of the hole in the wall. You line up your sights on the third armoured car in the line and squeeze the trigger. The Bren shakes as you fire and you find it hard to control. Looking down the sights you see that there is so much fire that it is difficult to tell if you have hit the car or not. You fire again, finger squeezing and holding the trigger. Sparks fly off the car and it suddenly stops.

A moment later a German emerges. You fire and he is killed, though you do not know if it was you or another paratrooper who killed him.

The armoured cars are being destroyed by the British fire and the road is soon strewn with burning vehicles, dead Germans and immobile armoured cars. Yet the Germans just keep coming. The half-tracks now try to push their way past the wrecks. You can see that these are packed with infantry, who start to tumble out and deploy on the road.

◊ *If you wish to fire on the infantry, then go to 94.*
◊ *If you wish to fire on the half-tracks, then go to 43.*

---

63 *Sunday, 7:30 p.m. – ½ hour to sunset...*
Having the Major breathing down your neck is one thing, but a Lt. Col. is just too much. You turn to Frost and explain to him that you are the kind of leader that needs room and you would be grateful if he didn't tag along with your platoon. Frost turns in your direction and you notice that he is going a strange colour of purple.

"The day I take orders from a Lieutenant," booms Frost, spittle collecting on his hairy lip, "is the day I give it all up and join the Bosch." It looks as though Lt. Col. Frost is coming along for the ride.

◊ *Go to 74.*

Tuesday, morning...

You duck out of the HQ building and head back down the street, hugging the walls and zipping into doorways where possible. You are waiting for the thump of a sniper's bullet with every step. You head south towards the river and are delighted when your platoon's house comes into view, surrounded by blackened houses. You relax as you get nearer. It is your final mistake. You feel nothing as a sniper's bullet enters your skull, and you flop down dead.

◊ *Operation Market Garden is over for you. Go to 68 to discover your fate.*

Monday, morning...

Though the bridge is blocked, German soldiers have spilled out of three half-tracks onto the bridge. These are now trying to organise themselves but have come under a lot of fire from all directions. You take another PIAT shell from the bag next to you and carefully place it into the front of the PIAT tube. It slips into place with ease and you once again glance through the sights. You aim to hit the road amongst a group of German soldiers and pull the trigger. The projectile pops from the PIAT and heads for the bridge. Again it is off target, falling just behind the men. However, the resultant explosion throws a couple of them to the ground.

You can see that the remaining Germans are running back across the bridge. You decide to save ammunition, not to fire at the fleeing Germans and instead watch as they disappear from view.

An eerie silence returns to the bridge and you look out of the hole in the wall to see a sight of devastation. The road is now blocked by burning and disabled vehicles; scattered amongst these are dead and dying Germans.

You look away from the scene as your training kicks in. You send Corporal Venables off to see if you have any casualties and tell him to warn the men to be ready for another attack. He disappears and returns shortly to say that no one is injured. The men in your room relax and you take the chance to walk around the house, going room to room, speaking to your men.

◊ *Go to 24.*

You stand in the hall of the house looking out across the road at the building you are about to attack. The roof has largely collapsed and the top two floors have been completely destroyed. However, the bottom two floors remain. The door has come off its hinges but has been pushed back in place. There are four windows in total looking out across the street. You can see that furniture has been pushed back up against these. Shadows flit about in the darkness inside.

You turn to Venables and ask if he is ready. He nods. You give the word and your Bren guns open up. You watch as bullets start spitting against the house opposite, aiming for the windows.

You give the word and start running. You are first, zigzagging across the street. The cobbles are slippery and the rubble makes it difficult to find firm footing. You hear gunfire from the windows opposite and dust spurts at your feet as bullets hit the ground.

Suddenly you are at the door. Without stopping you slam your boot into it. It flies backwards. You rush inside. As your eyes adjust to the gloom you can see stairs ahead of you and open doorways to your left and right.

◊ *To go left, go to 70.*
◊ *To go right, go to 10.*

67 *Sunday, night...*

The darkness of the night seems to have closed in on you and you suddenly find the silence unnerving. The Major has turned away and is consulting a map using a small torch that throws out a narrow, but intense beam of light. You stand for a moment unsure of what to do. The Major eventually sees you.

"Why are you still here?" he asks, his umbrella dangling from the elbow of the arm that holds the map. You start to explain that you just have a Section of men and that you are worried you will be killed. The Major turns quickly in your direction, whipping out his .455 calibre Webley Mk VI revolver.

"God damn you, man. If you don't go now, then God be my witness I will shoot you dead where you stand." You look into his eyes and decide that he is not joking. Sheepishly you call your men together and head for the steps that lead to the nearby bridge.

◊ *Go to 15.*

---

68 The Arnhem landings were a brutal and relentless battle. The soldiers that survived lived on their wits, followed their orders and most importantly were lucky! You have done well so far and have the makings of a good solider. However, if you wish to successfully capture and hold Arnhem Bridge for as long as possible, you need to think like a paratrooper – one of the toughest soldiers ever to live.

This time remember what Lt. Col. John Frost said after the battle:

"Some of my old soldiers and I have had many narrow shaves and been so nearly overwhelmed, but each time, fate or the God of Battles had intervened in our favour, but not this time and verily for us, Arnhem had been 'a drop too many'."

◊ *Now go back to section 1 and try again.*

Wednesday, morning...

You return to the platoon house and collect up the remaining men. Of the full platoon of more than thirty men you are left with just eight still able to fight. You tell the men the situation is desperate but you have been asked to help evacuate the injured paratroopers from the school.

You give the men fifteen minutes to prepare and then set off. You move quickly to the end of the road and turn right towards HQ. As you move down this road you can see a German tank sitting immobilized – its gun poking in the air at an unnatural angle. You duck past the tank and head south. At the bottom of the road you turn right, move past HQ and under the bridge.

As you move your men stay in a wide line. The streets are strewn with burned-out vehicles, debris, roof tiles and dead soldiers – both British and German.

Suddenly you see the school over a patch of overgrown grass and trees to the north. The building has been ravaged by the battle. The roof is in tatters and it looks as though it has been hit more than once with artillery. You are about to move through the grassy area when you spot a German tank on the bridge above. Its gun is in the process of releasing a round and you watch in horror as it slams into the side of the school.

◊ *If you wish to try and cross the grass and enter the school, go to 57.*

◊ *If you feel that you are outnumbered and a retreat would be the best option, go to 85.*

70

Tuesday, morning...

You swing to the left and enter the room. There are two German soldiers crouched at the windows, their guns spitting bullets into the street.

You decide that at such close range there is no need to aim your Sten, and fire from the hip. You squeeze the trigger – nothing happens! The gun clonks and jams!

The nearest German grins up at you. Then fires at point blank range.

The bullet slams into your chest throwing you backwards into the hall.

Light fades from your eyes. You have no idea how long you are unconscious, but when you open your eyes you see Corporal Venables crouching over you. You look at his hands and see they are dripping with blood.

"Hang on," he whispers.

You try to keep your eyes open, but all you want to do is sleep. Slowly you allow your eyes to close for the last time.

◊ *Operation Market Garden is over for you. Go to 68 to discover your fate.*

71

Tuesday, morning...

You scramble from the floor and scream for the PIAT. Another shell hits, throwing you to the floor again. This time part of the ceiling joist comes away and a nearby paratrooper is killed as the huge wooden beam smacks into his head. You drag yourself to your feet and head upstairs where the PIAT is located. You see Corporal Revie at the top of the stairs, staring wide-eyed. Another shell hits and you are thrown down three steps, but catch the handrail and heave yourself up.

As you reach the top of the stairs there is no sign of Revie, but through the dust you do see two bodies propped against the wall, as if sleeping. The next shell does real damage. The wall to your right crumbles – for a moment you are looking into blue sky. Then the wooden floor splinters and falls away from your feet. You throw your hands out to break your fall, but the room below has been reduced to rubble. You land badly on a pile of bricks with a crack. You are dead before the next shell hits.

◊ *You have joined the ranks of the glorious dead. Go to 68 to discover your fate.*

72 *Tuesday, morning...*

You duck out of the HQ building and head back down the street, hugging the walls and zipping into doorways where possible. You are waiting for the thump of a sniper's bullet with every step but it never comes. You reach the platoon house safely.

You burst through the door to be greeted by Venables, who is coming down the stairs. He stops halfway, looks directly at you with a fake scowl and asks, "I hope you didn't forget the wine, I think we are expecting visitors." He then puts his flattened hand to his top lip to mimic Hitler's moustache and walks down the final few steps with long outstretched legs doing an exaggerated goosestep. You smile.

◊ *Go to 22.*

---

73 *Sunday, 4.30 p.m. – 3 ½ hours to sunset...*

You pass the order to attack. A smoke screen will be laid down in the open ground ahead and 2 Section and 3 Section will lay down fire into the trees. 1 Section will attack through the smoke, over the open ground. Major Tatham-Warter takes the chance to signal the attack with a quick hoot on his bugle.

After instructing your mortar crew to lay down smoke you decide to join 1 Section in the attack and Corporal Revie seems pleased. 2 Section and

3 Section have already started to lay down fire and a steady stream of rifle shots whizz across the open ground towards the Germans. Soon the Bren machine guns open up, throwing even more fire into the small section of woods. It is not long before you hear the pop of your mortar and a light bluish smoke quickly fills your vision.

Before you can react 1 Section are away, and you find yourself running quickly across the open ground towards the enemy, German bullets fizzing through the air. You pump your arms – you must keep running! Suddenly the smoke makes way for trees. You hear Lee Enfield rifles firing to your left and right, but cannot see anything except for trees and the haze of smoke. Then you see a German. He is kneeling behind a tree, his rifle aimed away from you. You fire your Sten gun without aiming. A slight squeeze on the trigger allows a stream of bullets to snake out. The first couple miss the German, but then he is hit, his face becoming engulfed in a cloud of red, before he slumps forward, his gun still aiming. You sprint past his body into the woods.

By the time the smoke has cleared the Germans are all dead. It appears it was just a small company of men, perhaps ten or so. You find Corporal Revie who informs you that you have just one casualty. A private has been shot in the arm. You thank him for a well executed attack and trudge back to find Major Tatham-Warter on the road.

◊ *Go to 50.*

---

74 *Sunday, 8 p.m. – sunset...*
The presence of Frost keeps your men's minds focused, and progress from Oosterbeek is good.

It is starting to get dark as you pass the sign for Arnhem, and once again move from the countryside into a town. The Arnhem streets are deserted. You keep the river on your right-hand side and push on. Even in the gloom you can still make out the arches of Arnhem Bridge.

Frost is keen to keep your men moving. Whenever you spot Germans he directs you off the main streets, and through the gardens of houses and down back alleys. At one point you come across a group of about twenty German soldiers. Unseen by the enemy, Frost simply knocks on the door of a nearby house. When it is opened by an old lady, Frost pushes past her and leads you through her house, out of the backdoor, through her back garden and down the next street.

You carefully navigate your way through the town's streets. The sun has set by the time you finally reach the bridge.

◊ *Go to 80.*

Sunday, night...

You point to the pillbox and the soldier with the flame-thrower nods. Suddenly the black night is illuminated by a rod of yellow flame. It shoots from the nozzle over the gap and onto the bridge. Flame-throwers are not the easiest of weapons to use, and the flame misses the pillbox and instead hits the small wooden hut behind, setting it on fire.

The soldier stops firing and watches the hut. At first it is a small fire, but it quickly spreads. Suddenly there is a huge explosion as the hut disintegrates, throwing burning wood all across the bridge. A small smile forms on your lips as your realise the inexperienced Germans must have been using the hut to store their ammo. The paint of the nearby arches catches alight and soon the whole metal framework is burning – but there is no chance it will collapse.

You send the two soldiers away and settle in for the night, watching the fire tickle away at the bridge. After a while you fall asleep.

It is still dark when you are woken a few hours later by an explosion. You look out and see the bridge is still burning. A few German trucks had tried to cross over, but somehow they had caught alight and are now just burning hulks in the middle of the road.

◊ *Go to 41.*

---

76 A paratrooper should be the pride of the British forces, but you are letting the side down! If you are to make it as one of the best soldiers ever to fight for crown and country, you need to listen to your commander, fight with courage and, hopefully, have a hat full of luck.

So, stiff upper lip, paratrooper, and head over to section 1 to try again.

Sunday, 7:30 p.m. – ½ hour to sunset...
Your paratroopers are good men and you know that many of them will not get home alive. This may be the last chance they will have for a bit of fun, so you let them enjoy the moment.

After a few minutes, an old lady approaches you through the crowd. She is carrying a basket of apples and a large mug of frothy beer. She offers you the mug and you take it, thanking her. She passes you an apple and disappears back into the crowd. The beer is warm but tastes amazing. You find a small wall and sit down as the crowds push past.

Time passes quickly and your men become intermingled with the crowd. The bliss is finally broken by a gruff voice and you turn to see Major Tatham-Warter emerging from behind a group of school children.

"Lieutenant," he barks. "This is not a party. Get your men moving NOW!"

As he speaks he lifts his rolled umbrella in a motion that makes you think he is about to strike you, before changing his mind.

◊ *Go to 100.*

Sunday, 8:00 p.m. – sunset...

The light is now fading quickly. You sprint back through the underpass and order the 6-pounder to be brought forward. You then tell Corporal Revie of 1 Section and Corporal Ramsey of 3 Section to get their men forward and to put fire down on the armoured car. As the officers pass out their orders you return through the underpass.

You arrive to find Corporal Venables standing in the middle of the road over the body of his dead private. There is no sign of the armoured car in the gloom ahead.

The casualties are removed and then you issue orders for 2 Section to head along the road, 1 Section to spread out to the left and 3 Section to move round behind the houses on your right. As you round the bend bullets rake the road and you throw yourself to the ground, rolling into the undergrowth at the side of the road. You quickly crawl forward behind a low wall. This time it is not the armoured car. Instead, the machine gun fire is coming from a mound to the left. However, in the dark you can't pinpoint its position.

You glance around. Your men have found cover, but they are pinned down by the machine gun.

◊ *To order an attack, go to 83.*

◊ *To see what Major Tatham-Warter wishes you to do, go to 38.*

You turn to your men and simply say that it is every man for himself. You wish them luck and send them off to try to escape. You head upstairs, where a group of injured paratroopers are lying on the floor. One man points to the window.

You move over to see a tall paratrooper struggling up the nearby embankment to the bridge road. He is carrying a makeshift white flag which flops from his rifle. As he reaches the top where the tank is sitting, a burst of machine-gun fire cuts him down. A group of five German soldiers are standing on the left – one of them is still pointing his gun at the paratrooper. A German officer walks up to the soldier, draws a pistol from his holster and shoots him in the head.

You turn back from the window in shock and rest your back against the wall.

You don't remember falling asleep, but the next time you open your eyes the German officer you saw killing one of his own men stands over you. You stand up and face each other without speaking. The German then salutes. You pause, unsure what to do, and then return the salute. You are now a prisoner of war.

◊ *You have fought hard and commanded your men well – this is the end of the Battle of Arnhem for you. Now go to 36 to discover what happened in the real battle.*

Sunday, night...

Arnhem Bridge is an impressive structure. The road is supported by two huge iron arches that curve across the bridge allowing it to span the fast-flowing Rhine. The long, narrow road starts on the edge of Arnhem town and lifts above the surrounding houses as it gets closer to the bridge. The bridge road is held on high concrete pillars and it is under the safety of these pillars that you now gather.

There is no sign of any Germans. It appears 2nd Battalion have arrived almost intact and Lt.Col. Frost is bobbing about, congratulating the men on the success of the advance. A brief conversation with Major Tatham-Warter allows you to get a clearer picture of the situation. There is no sign of the Reconnaissance squadron. They were all riding jeeps and were due to be at the bridge three hours ago. The Major also explains that 3rd Battalion should be here and he is expecting them to arrive at any moment.

Frost instructs you to keep your men quiet and then ducks into the darkness with the Major. They soon return and start giving out orders. The plan is to set up a defensive perimeter around this end of the bridge. This means that Germans attacking from Arnhem or across the bridge can be beaten back. They are expecting 30 Corps to arrive next

morning and these will come from the south, which is the other side of the river. You must hold out until 30 Corps gets here.

Frost orders your men to take over a nearby house. It is a large building next to the bridge, with upper floors directly overlooking the road bridge. From there you will have a clear line of fire onto the bridge. You gather your men and head north to the house. You pause at the door, before Corporal Venables steps forward and thumps on it. An old man answers. You explain that you wish to use his house. At first he protests, but when he sees the soldiers in the street he shrugs and lets you in.

The house has three storeys and you order your men to prepare the windows that face over the bridge. They knock out the glass and reinforce the walls with nearby furniture. You are overseeing your men's efforts when word comes that Major Tatham-Warter wishes to speak to you.

◊ *Go to 2.*

---

81 *Sunday, 3:30 p.m. - 4 ½ hours to sunset...*
You give the order to fire. The soldier nearest to you fires off two quick shots, his trained hands instinctively pushing the bolt action forwards and backwards with each shot. The magazine of the Lee Enfield holds ten .303 inch bullets, but only two are fired.

Despite the German's erratic wobbling he makes an easy target. The first bullet hits him in the back and he tumbles to the ground. The second bullet catches him as he falls. Corporal Revie then orders a man to move forward and check the German, whilst the remainder of 1 Section wait for a reaction from the surrounding area. None comes.

Once it is clear that the German is dead and that there are no others about, you order 1 Section to drop behind you and move 2 Section into the lead. Their leader is Corporal Venables, a jolly Londoner who you've shared a few drinks and tales with. He positions his men in an arrowhead formation before you advance once again.

As you pass the dead German you pause to examine his body. His bleached white face looks up at you. He is about fifty, with silver hair. He reminds you of your own father.

◊ *Go to 34.*

Sunday, 4:30 p.m. – 3 ½ hours to sunset...

You choose a defensive formation and pass out the orders. 1 Section deploy to the left, with most men hidden in the woods nearest to you. 2 Section deploy immediately in front of you with 3 Section in the field to the right. At the intersection between the sections you place your two Bren machine guns.

It takes a couple of minutes for your men to deploy, and all the time fire is coming in from the trees that hide the Germans. However, your men eventually return fire. At first it is just the cracks of the Lee Enfields, but in time the shudder of the Bren guns adds to the racket. But the Germans keep firing. You send word to your mortar group to have a go at the Germans and soon you can hear their shells exploding; ripping through the trees.

In the confusion of the battle you lose track of time, but estimate your men have been engaged for at least thirty minutes. So far the casualties to your men have been light. You have seen a couple of blood-soaked boys from 2 Section staggering past you for treatment by the medics behind, but it seems to be going well. The fire from your men has the Germans pinned, though you can still hear the rattle of their machine gun.

Suddenly Major Tatham-Warter appears at your side. You are crouched in the undergrowth, just your eyes and maroon beret poking over a nearby bush. The Major stands above you. His long thin body almost daring the Germans to hit him. He stares at the battle for a moment, then looks down at you, says nothing and strolls away.

A few minutes later you see the men from 1 Platoon mustering behind your position. The Major is in discussion with their commander and is pointing to the German position. As you watch, 1 Platoon start to push past your men – you assume, in preparation to mount an attack across the open ground between you and the woods. A pop from the mortar is followed by the slow release of a bluish smoke ahead of your men. You give the order to cease fire and watch as 1 Platoon disappears into the smoke.

The attack is brief and after just a couple of minutes you can see about ten Germans being led at gunpoint back to your position. Each has their arms raised high above their head in surrender.

◊ *Go to 56.*

Sunday, 8:00 p.m. – sunset...

83

You are keen to get your men moving and decide to order an attack. Looking around you can see Corporal Venables lying in a ditch on the opposite side of the road. Three of his men lie next to him. For some reason Venables has his rifle slung on his back and instead has a pistol in one hand and his binoculars in the other. As you watch he pops up his head and whips the binoculars to his eyes. The movement alerts the machine gunner who sends a spray of bullets into the road just in front of Venables, causing the paratrooper to drop back to the safety of the ditch.

You shout over to the Corporal to get his men

moving. He hears your voice and looks in your direction, his face confused. You shout the order again. This time Venables shouts a response but you can't understand him. You need to be closer.

You wait a few seconds and then start the sprint across the open road to the ditch where Venables is hiding. You slip after the first few steps but soon get your legs pumping. The day is still warm and sweat streams from your forehead as the weight of your kit makes running difficult. It is not far and as you pick up speed it looks as though you will make it.

You never even hear the bullet that kills you. The machine gun's lethal projectile passes clean through your beret and into your skull.

◊ *Operation Market Garden is over for you. Go to 76 to discover your fate.*

---

84 *Tuesday, morning...*

You let out a sigh and after a moment's thought decide to change your plan. You point back in the direction you have come. Frank nods and you both bob down the street in that direction, ducking from doorway to doorway as you move. The streets are still quiet and you suddenly feel surprised that you have not come under sniper fire. Perhaps the Germans have retreated after all. Ahead you can see your destroyed platoon house to the left and a line of trees at the top of the road hide a view of the wide river beyond.

Suddenly Frank stops at the junction of two streets and hugs the wall of the nearest building. You do the same.

"Tank," he whispers, "just around the corner. It's close!"

◊ *If you wish to attack the tank, go to 45.*
◊ *If you wish to call it a day and not risk an attack, go to 93.*

Wednesday, morning...

The number of Germans you have seen is making you nervous and you can feel a tension in the air. You give the order to retreat and within a couple of minutes your men are ready to move.

You set off south and you are soon turning left onto the main road through the defended area. It is strewn with debris and you can make out three burned-out metallic heaps that you assume are German tanks.

Your men slip into the HQ without further incident. You find the unknown Major on the top floor of the HQ, after a harrowing journey up the stairs past a huge number of injured men. You explain that the German presence is too strong and he simply nods.

"Well, it is just about over," he says looking at

you. "Every man for himself I think." You nod in agreement.

You return downstairs, still shocked by the number of wounded paratroopers and pass the word to your men that they are to try and make their way to safety. They scurry about the injured men collecting ammunition and then share it out amongst the remains of the platoon. You shake the hand of each man in turn, and then send them off into the streets to try and find a route through the enemy lines.

You wait a few minutes and follow your men, praying that you will be able to make it past enemy lines…

◊ *You have fought hard and commanded your men well – this is the end of the Battle of Arnhem for you. Now go to 36 to discover what happened in the real battle.*

---

86 *Sunday, night…*

The first paratrooper to enter the room now takes the PIAT and places it carefully on the floor. He keeps one end under his feet, twists the tube-like weapon and pulls hard on the other end until there is a click. He then picks up the long green weapon and lifts it onto his shoulder so it points towards the corner of the room.

"I would move if I was you!" he laughs and

instructs you to leave the room.

From outside the room there is a flash and a thud of an explosion. You return to the room to find a huge hole where the window had been.

Behind you is the second man. The doughnut-shaped canister is now on his back like a backpack and he holds the gun-like nozzle of the flame-thrower, a small flame dancing at the end. You step forward as the men move towards the hole. You explain that you are the commanding officer in this room and you will direct the attack.

◊ *If you wish to instruct the man with the flame-thrower to attack the concrete pillbox, go to 75.*

◊ *If you wish to tell him to aim at the small wooden huts first, go to 7.*

Monday, night...

You decide to remain in the top room overlooking the bridge and try to settle down to get some rest in the rubble. Two paratroopers from 1 Section remain on guard, allowing you to try and get some sleep. In the darkness you can see houses all around you burning bright as the sporadic artillery bombardment causes them to catch alight. You slip into a fretful sleep, praying for the first time since you were a child.

◊ *Go to 17.*

Sunday, night...

You return to the house to find your platoon disheartened by the failed attack and lost men. You climb to the top floor of the three-storey house. It is positioned to the right of the bridge and is immediately next to the bridge road. In fact, when you look out of the top floor window you are almost level with the bridge road. Just ahead of you is the pillbox and collection of small wooden huts. In the gloom of the night you can just make out the bodies of your dead paratroopers scattered in the road.

You watch out of the window for about an hour. The night is cool and in the silence you can hear the river lapping on the bank. Nothing moves on the bridge. The peace is broken by the sound of movement downstairs. You hear men talking loudly and the stomping of boots as they head to your room.

You are watching the door when two paratroopers enter. They are both carrying heavy weapons. The first to enter has a PIAT anti-tank gun slung over his shoulder, while the second is struggling with a lifebuoy flame-thrower and its heavy doughnut-shaped fuel canister. Before you can speak the first man addresses you.

"Sir, Major Tatham-Warter has ordered us to flame the pillbox." As he speaks the paratrooper points through the narrow window to the bridge outside. You weigh up the situation and then point to the PIAT and ask why it has also been brought.

"To make the hole bigger," says the second man in a thick Geordie accent.

◊ *If you wish to refuse to let the paratroopers blow a hole in the wall, go to 58.*

◊ *If it seems like a good idea, then go to 86.*

Tuesday, morning...

As you contemplate your next move, Major Tatham-Warter strolls in through the front door of the house. He is walking casually, umbrella swinging at his side. If you did not know better you would think he was out for an afternoon stroll. Behind the Major is a paratrooper lugging a PIAT. They both stop and turn to face you.

"This is Captain Tony Frank from A Company," says the Major. "He is going to rid us of those pesky tanks, but he needs someone to give him a hand on his tank hunt." As the Major stops speaking he looks directly at you.

◊ *Go to 35.*

Sunday, 6:45 p.m. – 1 hour and 15 minutes to sunset...
The crowds have now disappeared and you are
walking through deserted streets on the outskirts
of Oosterbeek. Ahead you can see a raised
embankment that carries the railway across the
road. A narrow underpass cuts under the railway.

You pass the order to approach with care and
2 Section are the first through the narrow tunnel.
You are only a few paces behind when you hear
the unmistakeable rattle of German machine gun
fire and the sudden cries of injured men.

As you sprint into the short tunnel, Sten gun
at the ready, you can hear the echoes of your
Lee Enfields coming from the other side of the
darkness. The light brings horror. About 200
metres ahead you see a German armoured car
sitting proudly in a bend in the road, its machine
gun spitting fire. Just ahead, you see the body of
a paratrooper from 2 Section; a second man lies in
the undergrowth clutching his own mangled hand.

To the right are three houses. In front of the
houses is a low wall that protects three gardens.
Corporal Venables is behind this wall, directing the
rest of his men to fire on the armoured car.

◊ *If you wish to pass the order for the 6-pounder anti-
tank gun to be brought forward, go to 40.*
◊ *If you wish to pull 2 Section back and go on the
defensive, go to 16.*

Sunday, night...

Despite the loss of 3 Section you are sure that an attack is the best option. Fighting your fear you rise to your feet. Bullets slice through the air all around you as you scream for your men to attack.

The paratroopers of 2 Section who lie in the road are reluctant to move but seeing your example they lift themselves to their feet. Fire is now coming in from the left as 1 Section target the pillbox, and you can see bullets slamming into the concrete causing pieces of brick and dust to spout up. Suddenly the German firing stops and you stand isolated in the middle of the road. They must have killed the gunner!

You level your Sten gun at the silent pillbox, fire a burst into the concrete and race forward. A cry of, "Airborne!" rips from your lungs.

You are only a few paces from the pillbox when the machine gun opens fire. The flash from the gun illuminates the faces of the Germans who sit in the darkness behind. You push on. A bullet hits you in the shoulder, stopping your run. You realise the gun was just reloading! You take one more step before you are hit again and topple forward, dying with the thunder of the German machine gun ringing in your ears.

◊ *Operation Market Garden is over for you. Go to 76 to discover your fate.*

Wednesday, morning...

You suddenly feel very tired indeed. Your head aches and your arm is throbbing with pain. You get the attention of the medic and ask if he has any painkillers. He smiles softly and disappears into the back. You look around the room and count twenty-five injured paratroopers before you give up. You know some of them and smile when they look at you. The wounds are horrific and you can see young boys with limbs missing, eyes gouged out and large patches of red covered by dirty bandages.

The doctor reappears with a small syringe and kneels next to you. He pulls up your sleeve and you feel a small prick as he injects the painkiller directly into your bloodstream.

"Morphine," he says.

You allow yourself to drift off to sleep.

When you wake it is dark and you can see a tall man silhouetted in the door. His uniform looks strange and it takes you a drug-soaked moment to realise he is German. You jerk forward and scramble for your Sten. It is gone. You start to panic and the German looks in your direction as you try to lift to your feet.

"Englander, the war is over for you. Your men have surrendered." He speaks in broken English. You slowly look around the room to see a number of German soldiers all holding rifles.

You allow your body to relax and slip back to the floor.

◊ *You have fought hard and commanded your men well – this is the end of the Battle of Arnhem for you. Now go to 36 to discover what happened in the real battle.*

Tuesday, morning...

You peek around the corner and see the tank about 40 metres away. It is sitting in the middle of the street, its engine chugging slowly. The house on the opposite side of the road has a low garden wall in front, though it is blackened and mostly rubble, it will be a good place to fire the PIAT.

Frank jams the PIAT between his feet, twists and pulls until it clicks. He then peeks around the corner before sprinting across the road and kneeling behind the low wall. You wait, watching.

"Ammo," he hisses.

Suddenly you have a very bad feeling about what is going to happen. Your stomach tightens and the hairs on your arms stand on end. You lean forward and shout to Frank to come to you. He looks puzzled but hurries back across the road.

You explain that the situation is too dangerous. You tell him that it is all too easy. That it is strange that there have been no snipers or German shelling. You explain that you are going to return to the Major. Frank stands amazed.

"Look, Sir," he says spitting the words, "you can do as you please." He then grabs the bag from your hand and ducks back around the corner.

You have little option left but to return to HQ without Frank.

◊ *Go to 13.*

Though the bridge is blocked, German soldiers
have spilled out of three half-tracks onto
the bridge. These are now trying to organise
themselves, but have come under a lot of fire from
all directions. You squint down the sights and
squeeze the trigger. The gun jerks, firing a few
bullets, then stops. You're out of ammo! You snatch
out the curved magazine that thrusts from the top
of the gun and replace it with a full one that lies
next to you. Looking back down the sights you can
see that many of the Germans have already been
shot and those left are running back across the
bridge. You aim the gun and fire at the fleeing men.
Two Germans jerk, throwing their arms into the air
as they fall to the ground. You keep firing, but the
metal framework is soon in the way and you stop.

An eerie silence returns to the bridge. The road
is blocked by burning and disabled vehicles; dead
and dying Germans litter the ground.

You look away from the scene as your training
kicks in. You send Corporal Venables off to see if
you have any casualties, and tell him to warn the
men to be ready for another attack. He disappears
and returns shortly to say that no one is injured.
You take the chance to walk around the house,
going from room to room, speaking to your men.
◊ *Go to 24.*

Sunday, 3:30 p.m. – 4 ½ hours to sunset...

You are keen to keep pushing on along Lion Route. Your platoon is surrounded on all sides by woods. 1 Section is out in front in a narrow arrowhead formation, 2 Section and 3 Section follow on behind you in line. Progress is slow at times and you find yourself urging Corporal Revie to pick up the pace. Revie is a good soldier, with a face like stone, but he is cautious.

Eventually the woods start to thin out, and the roads widens slightly as houses begin to appear on the left and right. They look different from those in England. They have a boxed shape with square window and steep orange tiled roofs. A sign tells you that you are entering Doorwerth. Progress through the village is fast and you encounter no Germans. In fact it feels more like a ghost town, with the streets deserted despite it being a warm day.

Suddenly a German soldier appears out of a side road just a few yards ahead of your men. He is riding a rickety bike. When he sees your men he tries to quickly pedal the heavy bike away, but instead wobbles precariously across the street. Your men freeze, unsure of what to do.

◊ *If you wish to order 1 Section to fire, then go to 81.*
◊ *If you wish to try and capture the German, then go to 29.*

96 *Sunday, night...*

Anger races through your body as you watch the Major turn his back. You have just watched your men die and you know they deserve a decent burial. You sprint forward and grab the Major by the arm. Pulling hard you swing him around so he is facing you. Screaming in his face you tell him you will mount your own attack to recover the bodies.

The Major remains calm and simply lifts his left hand and places it on your shoulder. You feel a calm flood into your body.

"I understand," he says looking you in the eye. "But if you go back up there now more men will be killed." You stand for a minute or two staring at the Major and begin to realise he is right. You try to stammer an apology but he just smiles and orders you back to your men.

◊ *Go to 88.*

---

97 *Sunday, 3:00 p.m. – 5 hours to sunset...*

You turn and pass the order to attack the vehicles as they come down the road. You explain to your three section Corporals that you want all of the men to storm out of the trees and overwhelm the armoured car and truck. They look at you strangely as you give the order, but you lift your hand before they can complain.

Moments later the whole of 4 Platoon crouches in the undergrowth, hidden from the Germans. A German stands in the turret of the armoured car, his finger at the trigger of his machine gun. You check that your Sten gun's safety catch is off, wait for the car to draw level and then scream for your men to attack.

You are the first out of the undergrowth, gun at your hip, bullets spitting as you squeeze the trigger. The noise is deafening as the bullets bounce off the armoured car. For a moment it seems as though your plan is working. Then the armoured car suddenly speeds forward, moving quickly away from the attack. But as it moves, the truck behind stops and you see a squad of German soldiers jumping down from the back!

You watch as the turret of the armoured car turns in your direction and the machine gun begins to fire. Corporal Ramsey of 3 Section is hit first, then a paratrooper to your right is hit – a bullet passing through his neck, splashing warm blood on your face. You are hit in the chest. As you fall to the floor the world is strangely silent.

◊ *Operation Market Garden is over for you. Go to 76 to discover your fate.*

Wednesday, morning...

You are woken by the sound of distant gunfire. It is early, but the sun is already up. You look out of the window to see that most of the surrounding houses are still smouldering and the thud of artillery shows the Germans have not given up.

You try to scrounge something to eat, but are quickly informed by the men in your platoon that there is no food. Instead, you decide to make your way to HQ. You duck out of the house and head left, away from the river. You crouch down as you run – dodging from crumbled doorway to burning building. The roads are choked with debris and the occasional dead paratrooper.

You arrive at the HQ to find a sight from hell. Everywhere you look there are wounded soldiers lying on the floor. The bloody faces, smashed limbs and bleeding bodies leave you feeling sick inside.

You make your way to a room upstairs, where there are several officers. You are greeted by a Major you do not recognise, though you think he may be from the 9th Field Company.

"The situation is pretty grim," the Major says. He is a small man with sandy hair. His face is smeared with black soot. "30 Corps are not going to arrive, we have almost run out of ammo and the Krauts are knocking on the door."

You pause, unsure what to do next, but decide

to ask what you and your men can do to help.

"Well, we have two problems. We need men to go and help get the injured out of the school to the north before it is overrun. We have also had reports that the Jerries have placed explosives on the bridge supports on this side of the river."

◊ *If you wish to go to the school, go to 69.*
◊ *If you wish to go to the bridge, go to 9.*

Tuesday, morning...

You head east, away from the destroyed platoon house but closer to the Germans.

You set off, crouching low as you run from doorway to doorway. The street is wide and cobbled with narrow pavements on both sides. They are flanked by large town houses each three or four storeys tall. You cross the streets without catching sight of a tank or any Germans. The sun is high in the sky and the town seems strangely pleasant. The street runs south and you come to a T-junction. To the right you can see the bridge and the HQ building. To the left a wide road leads towards the German positions.

You pause and Frank taps you on the shoulder.

"Eh, mate, are you sure this is the right way?"

◊ *To continue east towards the Germans, go to 25.*
◊ *To head back towards the destroyed platoon house, go to 84.*

Sunday, 7:30 p.m. – ½ hour to sunset...

You locate Corporal Venables in the crowd of people ahead. His round face beams at you and you can see red lipstick on his cheek mixing in with the black camouflage paint. You order Venables to get his men moving, reminding him that you are fighting a war. He smiles and pushes back through the crowd, a pistol now in his right hand. Venables appears a few metres ahead of you, screaming at his men to get moving and within a few minutes you are once again pushing forward.

You are not on the main road through Oosterbeek and have instead skirted around the town keeping the river to your right. The crowds quickly thin out as you move forward. You have been marching steadily through the town streets for about ten minutes when you hear a dull thud in the distance to your right. Looking out over the trees you can see smoke rising from the railway bridge that spans the river just south of Oosterbeek.

◊ *If you wish to head down towards the river to see what has happened, then go to 21.*

◊ *If you wish to continue the advance, go to 39.*

BATTLE BOOKS
BEHIND THE SCENES

The author: GARY SMAILES

I decided to write the Battle Books series after becoming really annoyed that someone had not already got off their backsides and written them for me. You see, battles are just so great to read about – all the weapons and action – in fact, I don't understand why there aren't more books about them…

I live on the Wirral, which many years ago was inhabited by real-life Vikings. Sometimes, when I'm writing and I get stuck, I go out for a walk with my (stinky) dog. I imagine I'm part of a Viking army defending my land.

If I could have three wishes, one would be that I was a Viking, and the other would be to own a Viking longboat. The third would be that my dog didn't smell so much!

The artist: DAVID COUSENS

I'm David, and I drew the artwork in *Battle Books: Arnhem*. I do a lot of work producing tutorials for budding illustrators, which are featured in magazines. Drawing something like *Battle Books: Arnhem* is great because it's not every day that someone asks you to draw battle illustrations.

ROUGH   FINAL

The piece above is from paragraph 92, when you are receiving treatment after being shot. I sketched the rough in blue (this is a black-and-white book, so you can't see the blue lines), which makes it easier to go over later in black ink. I'm also careful to leave space for the text. I inked the final and filled using grey. Little touches, like leaving the edges of the background rough, add to the gritty atmosphere. I've also included some extra "blood splatter" effects using an Adobe® Photoshop brush.

BATTLE BOOKS

Take up your weapons and prepare to fight your own battle...

978 1 4451 0112 5

978 1 4451 0113 2

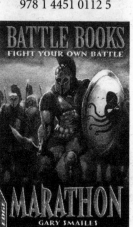

978 1 4451 0114 9

978 1 4451 0115 6